Hands Together

*52 Czech folk-tunes
arranged for piano by*

PETR EBEN

To buy Faber Music publications or to find out about the full range of titles available
please contact your local music retailer or Faber Music sales enquiries:

Faber Music Limited, Burnt Mill, Elizabeth Way, Harlow, CM20 2HX England
Tel: +44 (0)1279 82 89 82   Fax: +44 (0)1279 82 89 83
sales@fabermusic.com   fabermusicstore.com

FABER *ff* MUSIC

PUBLISHER'S NOTE

Czechoslovakia has a rich and diverse heritage of folk-tunes, many of which have a vigorous quality that is particularly attractive to young pianists. These fifty-two pieces are selected from a volume of one hundred by the distinguished Czech composer, Petr Eben, originally published in Prague. The tunes are given simple but inventive arrangements which often illustrate their descriptive titles. They are carefully graded (Grades 1 to 3), progressively introducing new technical elements.

Petr Eben, born in South Bohemia in 1929, has pursued a notable teaching career at Charles University, Prague, alongside his principal activities as composer and pianist. His concern for young musicians is reflected in his Czech adaptation of Orff's Schulwerk and a large number of compositions for children. His creative arrangements of folk-tunes have already proved a great success with piano teachers and pupils in Czechoslovakia; they will delight all those who enjoy, for example, the Bartók and Kodály arrangements of East European folk material.

CONTENTS

Hands Together

1. The cat is crawling down the hole

2. The girl with the blue eyes

3. Run, little duck

Allegro

4. The rejected lover

Poco presto

5. The careless shepherdess

Allegretto

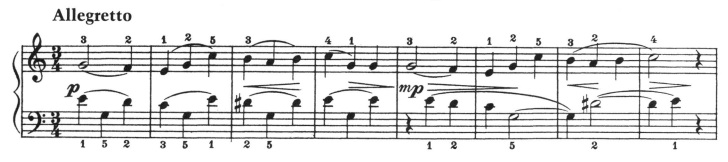

6. O, how it's raining

Vivace

7. On an old Prague bridge

Allegretto scherzando

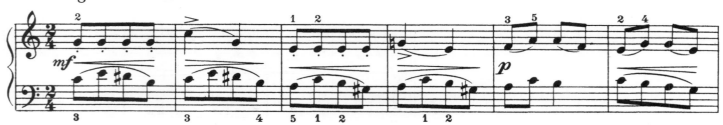

8. The Podebrady gate

Poco andante

9. Shepherds, you rascals!

Risoluto

6

10. Here comes the postman!

Allegro

11. The huntsman and the maidens

Tempo di marcia

12. Protect me, mother dear!

Allegretto tenero

13. Roses at the cottage window

Allegretto

14. Hey geese, come out of the wheat!

15. O, the scent of roses!

16. Parting

Andantino

17. The squire's meadow

Tempo di marcia

18. I have horses, coal-black horses

Allegretto ben ritmico

19. Have you done the ploughing, son?

Andante

20. The bagpipes sound

21. Where were you, my Anulienka?

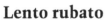

22. Strike up, fiddlers!

23. Hushabye, my little angel

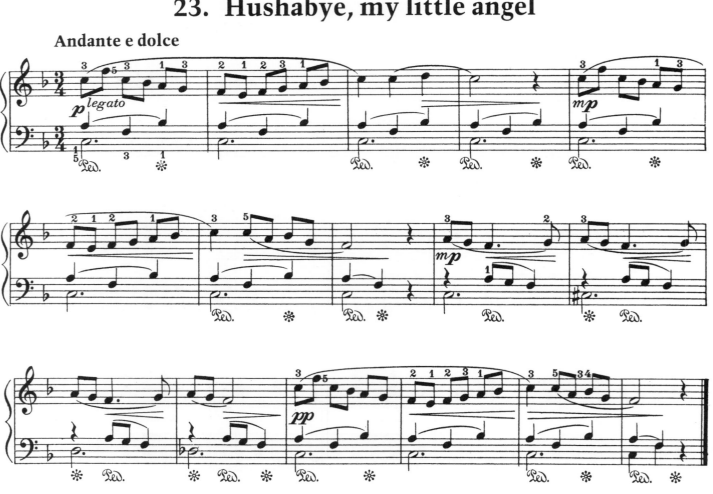

24. The bells of Bechyne

25. The horses are grazing

26. Johnny was grazing three oxen

27. Lament

28. The moonlight betrayal

Andante triste

29. Come inside, boys!

Tempo di minuetto

30. The goose-girl in winter

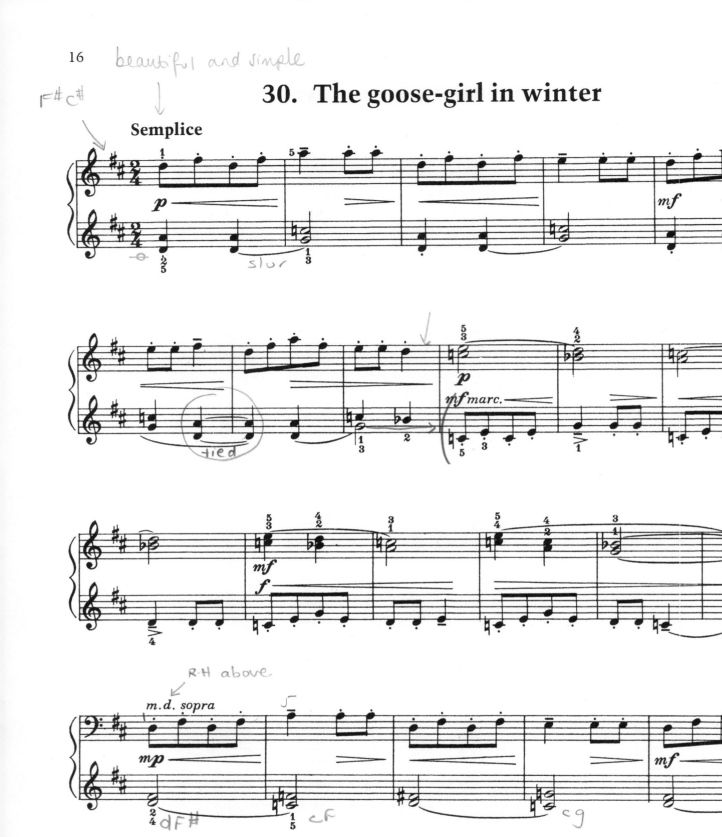

31. How fickle is love!

Andante

32. The gosling's first flight

Con moto

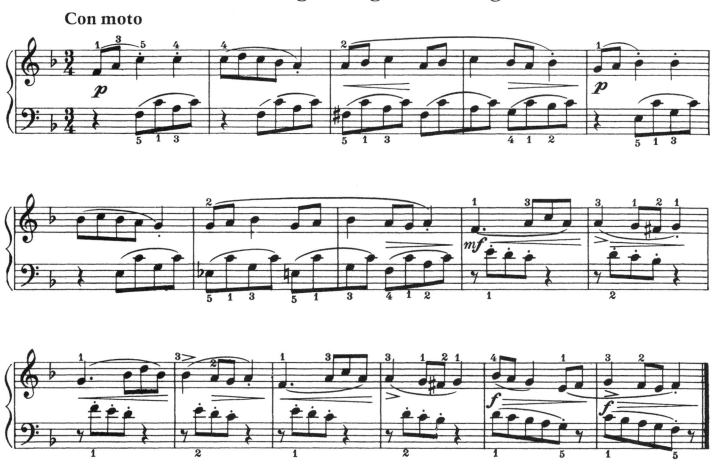

33. Johnny's upset my basket

Allegro scherzando

34. The blacksmith hammers all night long

Comodo e risoluto

35. Beware of marrying young

36. Angela, be mine

37. How happy we used to be!

Con moto

38. Our old stove is bust again

Allegro

39. Clickety clackety go my hobnails

Allegro giocoso

40. Where have you been, little cuckoo?

Allegro moderato

41. If only he were here!

Poco andante

42. Dark eyes, go to sleep

Andantino tenero

43. Don't be angry!

Andante, ma animato

44. Under the oak tree

45. My sweetheart has forgotten me

46. I am a jolly fellow

47. There's a pear tree in the meadow

Con calore, tranquillo

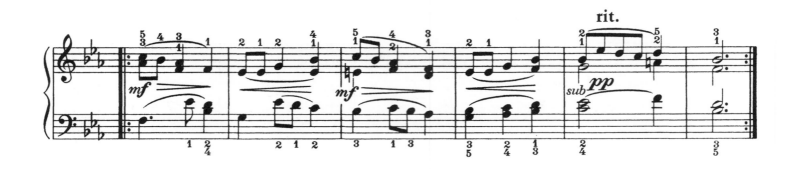

48. The horses await the ploughman

Tempo di marcia

49. How I love you, Johnny!

50. Goodnight, my love

51. Whose are those geese?

Poco andante

52. I sowed wheat

Moderato semplice